Tom and Ricky

and the

Secret Staircase

Bob Wright

High Noon Books
Novato, California

Cover Design: Nancy Peach
Interior Illustrations: Herb Heidinger

International Standard Book Number: 0-87879-328-3

9 8 7 6 5 4
20 19

You'll enjoy all the High Noon Books. Write for
a free full list of titles.

Contents

CHAPTER 1

A Broken Wheel

Ricky looked at his bike. The front wheel was broken. He had gone over some boxes. Now he couldn't ride it. It looked bad.

"What happened to your bike?" Tom called.

"I went over some boxes. I didn't see them," Ricky answered.

"Can you fix it?" Tom asked.

"I tried but it is bad," Ricky answered.

"How much will it cost to get it fixed?" Tom asked.

"About $15," Ricky answered.

"That's a lot," Tom said.

"It sure is," Ricky answered.

"Maybe we can earn some money. That way we could pay for it," Tom said.

Ricky's mother came into the yard. She saw the broken front wheel. Even Patches, Ricky's dog, was looking at it.

"How are we going to fix it?" she asked.

"Well, I thought I could do some work. Some people around here might need some help. Maybe I could help some people clean their yards," Ricky said.

"Hey, Ricky," Tom said. "What about Mr. Bell's yard? There are lots of weeds there."

"Maybe we can both work," Ricky said.

Mr. Bell lived down the street. He lived in a very big, old house. He lived there all alone. He was old. He couldn't do any yard work by himself.

"I don't think Mr. Bell has any money. He used to keep that yard looking so nice. Why don't you do it for free?" Ricky's mom asked.

"But we want to get some money for my bike," Ricky said.

"Here's what we'll do," she said. "If you and Tom help Mr. Bell, your dad and I will pay you. I think Mr. Bell will be very happy to see his yard all cleaned up."

"That sounds like a good idea," Tom said.

"Tom, can you help me?" Ricky asked.

"Sure. We'll do it together," Tom said.

Ricky was thinking. Mr. Bell didn't go out of his house very much. He stayed in that old house all the time. He used to keep the yard looking so nice. No one saw much of him. He didn't talk to people when he did come out. Maybe he might not want his yard cleaned up.

"What if Mr. Bell says not to clean his yard?" Ricky asked.

"Why not go and ask him?" Ricky's mother said.

"Let's go," Ricky said.

Patches jumped up. He wanted to go wherever Tom and Ricky went.

CHAPTER 2

Mr. Bell

Tom went slowly on his bike. Ricky walked along with him. Patches walked next to Ricky. Mr. Bell's house wasn't too far away.

There was a big fence all around Mr. Bell's house. There were weeds all over the yard. It hadn't been cleaned in a long time. Tom and Ricky looked at all the weeds.

"That's a lot of work," Tom said.

"It sure is," Ricky answered.

"Well, let's go," Tom said.

They opened the gate and walked up to the door. Patches was right in back of them.

They rang the door bell. No one answered. They rang it again. Still no one answered. They could hear someone walking around in the house.

"Maybe he doesn't want to answer the doorbell," Tom said.

"Maybe he can't hear it," Ricky said.

"Try again," Tom said.

Still no one came to the door.

"Let me bang on the door," Ricky said.

After a minute the door opened. There was an old man. "Can I help you boys?" he said. Mr. Bell seemed nice.

6

*After a minite the door opened.
There was an old man.*

"We live near you, Mr. Bell. We would like to help you clean up your yard," Ricky said.

"What did you say?" Mr. Bell asked.

"We live near you. We want to help clean up your yard," Ricky said.

"How much will it cost?" Mr. Bell asked.

"It won't cost anything," Tom said.

"I'm sorry, boys. I don't hear very well," Mr. Bell said.

Tom spoke louder. "It won't cost anything."

"Well, that is very nice. But why do you want to help me?" Mr. Bell asked.

"I need to get my bike fixed. My mother said if I help you, she will pay me," Ricky said.

"And I'm going to help him," Tom said.

8

"I used to keep the yard looking so nice," Mr. Bell said. "Now I am old. I can't do that work anymore."

"We can come every day after school," Tom said.

"Come on in, boys," Mr. Bell said.

Tom and Ricky went inside the house with Mr. Bell. It was very big. Everything was old. There were many books and lots of chairs.

"My grandfather built this house. I have lived here all my life," Mr. Bell said.

"We can start tomorrow," Ricky said.

"That will be fine," Mr. Bell answered.

Tom and Ricky left Mr. Bell's house. Tom got his bike. He went slowly.

Ricky and Patches walked along with him.

When they got home, Ricky's mother said, "How did it go?"

"Mr. Bell is very nice. He is happy that we are going to clean his yard," Ricky said.

"It was hard for him to hear. We had to talk very loud," Tom said.

"That's why he stays in his house most of the time," Ricky's mother said. "He doesn't hear very well."

"Why does he live in that house all by himself?" Ricky asked.

"I'll tell you all about that," she answered.

CHAPTER 3

The Old House

Ricky's mother started to tell Tom and Ricky about Mr. Bell and the old house.

"Mr. Bell's grandfather built that house over 100 years ago. He has a grandson who lives a long way from here. Steve, his grandson, doesn't come here very much. People say there is gold hidden in that old house. They say Mr. Bell's grandfather hid it after he built the house," she said.

"How much gold?" Ricky asked.

"Some people say there is a lot of gold hidden there. Other people don't think there is any. Mr. Bell is very poor. He has looked and looked for the gold," she said.

"I don't think there could be any gold. Mr. Bell has lived there all his life, but he hasn't found it," Tom said.

"Well, I heard once that it is hidden in a secret place," she said.

"A secret place?" Ricky asked.

"Yes. I heard that there is a hidden staircase in the house. The staircase goes to a room where the gold is," she said.

"Where did Mr. Bell's grandfather get the gold?" Tom asked.

"A long time ago people didn't save money. They saved gold," she answered. "Mr. Bell's grandfather was very rich. He owned all the land around here."

"But what about the hidden staircase?" Ricky asked.

"When the grandfather built the house he wanted to keep all his gold there. Somewhere in that old, big house there are stairs hidden behind a wall. There is a way to open a door to walk up those stairs," she said.

"Why doesn't Mr. Bell open all the doors to find the stairs?" Tom asked.

"Well, that may seem easy but it is not," she said.

"Why?" Tom asked.

"Mr. Bell's grandfather didn't use a real door. He hid the stairs in back of something like a wall. You can't tell there are stairs. You have to know how to open the special door to find the stairs," she said.

"What do you think about the gold?" Ricky asked.

"I think it would be nice for Mr. Bell," she said.

"Well, we will start helping Mr. Bell tomorrow," Ricky said.

"Right. Maybe there is gold in the weeds," Tom said.

They all laughed.

"Right. Maybe there is gold in the weeds."

CHAPTER 4

Cleaning The Yard

Tom and Ricky went to Mr. Bell's house right after school. They banged hard on the door so he could hear them. When he opened the door he looked happy. Maybe he had been thinking they might not come to help him.

"Hi, Mr. Bell. We're here to get started," Ricky said.

"Where should we start?" Tom asked.

"Well, let's see. Why not start by the front gate?" Mr. Bell said.

"Where do you want us to put the weeds?" Ricky asked.

"Just put them in a big pile. Then we can clean them up at the same time," Mr. Bell said.

Mr. Bell walked with Tom and Ricky to the front gate.

"You can work for about an hour today. Let's see how much you can do. I won't be able to work with you today. I have someone with me in the house," he said.

Mr. Bell started to walk back to the house. Then he stopped and turned around. "Let me show you the side door to the house. You can come in if you want a drink of water. It is a hot day," he said.

Mr. Bell took Tom and Ricky around to the side of the house. "This door goes into the kitchen. The door is broken. I can't close it all the way. Just come in if you want," he said.

Tom and Ricky went back to start weeding. There were lots of weeds. It didn't seem they were getting much done.

"This is more work than I thought," Ricky said.

"It sure is. Look at all the weeds we've pulled up. But it doesn't seem like we've even started," Tom said.

After they had worked for a while, Tom said, "I'd like a glass of water. How about you?"

"Sure," Ricky answered.

They went around to the side of the house. They pushed on the kitchen door and it opened. Mr. Bell had put two glasses by the sink. Everything looked old in the kitchen.

Ricky filled his glass with water. Then they heard yelling from another room in the house. They could hear Mr. Bell and someone else. They didn't know what to do. They heard the front door open and close. Then it was quiet.

Mr. Bell came into the kitchen. He saw the boys. His face was red. He looked mad.

"I'm sorry. That was my grandson. He came to see me. He needs money but I don't have any. He thinks I'm rich. He got mad and left," Mr. Bell said.

*They heard someone yelling. They could hear
Mr. Bell and someone else.*

"It was so hot we came in to get a glass of water," Ricky said.

"Let's see how you're doing," Mr. Bell said.

They all walked out to the front gate.

"It is starting to look nice again," Mr. Bell said.

"There is still lots to do," Ricky said.

"Why don't you stop for today? Can you come back tomorrow?" Mr. Bell asked.

"We sure can. We'll come again after school," Tom said.

"See you tomorrow," Ricky said.

Tom and Ricky left to go home. They liked Mr. Bell. He really was a nice man.

CHAPTER 5

A Bad Surprise

The next day Tom and Ricky went back to Mr. Bell's house. Ricky hoped they would be done soon. He wanted to get his bike fixed.

They looked at the yard with all the weeds.

"I don't think we're ever going to finish this work," Tom said.

"It is a lot of work. Maybe we don't have to get all the weeds," Ricky said.

It was a hot day again. Today they worked faster. They wanted to hurry and get done.

They liked Mr. Bell, but they weren't sure if they liked all that weeding.

Tom wanted a glass of water after a little while. They both went to the side door of the big house. The house was very quiet.

"Do you think we should let Mr. Bell know we're here?" Tom asked.

"That's all right. Maybe he saw us. He knew we were going to be here," Ricky said.

"I'll call very loud. That way he'll know we're here," Tom said.

Tom went to the door going into the next room. He called out, very loud, "Mr. Bell. Mr. Bell, we're here . . . "

Then Tom stopped. "Ricky, come here!"

Ricky ran to the door. He pushed it open.

They saw Mr. Bell in the next room lying on the floor. He wasn't moving. It looked like he had fallen down. They ran over to him.

"You stay here, Tom. I'll run home," Ricky said.

"No. Let me go. I have my bike. I can go faster on it. I'll call the hospital to come and get him," Tom said.

Tom ran out of the house to his bike.

Mr. Bell's eyes were closed. But Ricky could tell he was alive.

Tom came running back in. "I called the hospital. They have men coming here. They are going to take Mr. Bell to the hospital," he said.

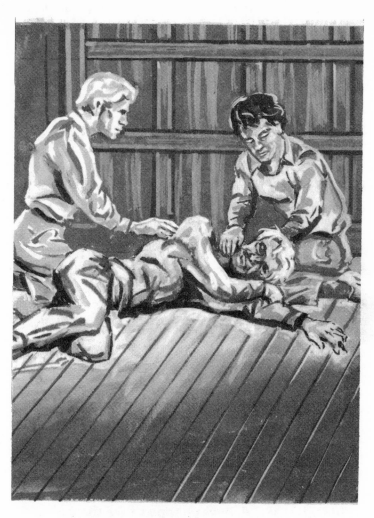

*Mr. Bell's eyes were closed. But Ricky could
tell he was alive.*

The hospital men came to the side door. One of them said, "Do you boys know what happened?"

"No. We are working for Mr. Bell. We found him here on the floor," Ricky said.

The hospital men got Mr. Bell up and carried him out. They took him to the hospital.

Tom and Ricky went back to Ricky's house. Ricky called the hospital.

The nurse said, "Mr. Bell had a bad fall. He will have to stay here for a while. He can see people tomorrow."

The next day Tom and Ricky went to the hospital. Mr. Bell was happy to see them.

"How's the yard coming along?" he asked.

"We didn't go there today, Mr. Bell," Ricky said.

"That's OK. I'm glad to see both of you," he said.

"Is there anything you need?" Tom asked.

"Well, yes, there is. It would help me if you could get my glasses. I can't read without them. They might be in the kitchen. If they are not there, look in the living room," he said.

"We'll be glad to get them for you," Ricky said.

"Thanks for coming," Mr. Bell said.

CHAPTER 6

Strange Noises

Tom and Ricky went right back to Mr. Bell's house. Tom put his bike by the front gate. He started to put his lock on it.

"You don't have to lock it. We'll only be gone for a few minutes," Ricky said.

Tom put the lock on anyway. "I'm used to locking it," he said.

Tom and Ricky went around to the side door. They pushed the kitchen door open and went in. Patches went in with them.

"Now, let's see. Mr. Bell said he left his glasses on the kitchen table," Ricky said.

The glasses weren't there. Tom put the key to his bike lock on the table. They looked all over the big room. No glasses anywhere.

"Well, Mr. Bell said that maybe they were in the next room," Ricky said.

They left the kitchen. They had never been in the rest of the house. They went from room to room looking for the glasses. They looked everywhere. They could not find the glasses.

Then Ricky stopped. "Wait a minute, Tom. Did you hear anything?"

Tom and Patches both stopped.

"No. I don't hear anything," Tom said.

They all stood there. It was quiet.

Then Ricky said, "Listen. There it is again. I think I hear someone else in the house. It sounds like someone is walking around."

Patches barked.

"Shut up, Patches. Be quiet," Ricky said.

It was still quiet. Then Tom said, "I do hear something."

The noise sounded like someone was walking above them. It was not loud. But they could hear it when they were quiet.

"I think we better go," Ricky said.

"That's OK with me," Tom said.

They walked quietly back to the kitchen.

"What about Mr. Bell's glasses?" Tom said

"We'll tell him we couldn't find them. Maybe he remembers where he did leave them," Ricky said.

They went back out the kitchen door.

"Ricky, I left my key to the lock in the house," Tom said.

"Where?" Ricky asked.

"I think I put it on the kitchen table," Tom said.

They went back to the side door. The key wasn't on the table.

"Tom, are you sure you put it there?" Ricky asked.

"Yes, I am. I remember putting it there," Tom said.

"Do you think you picked it up? Maybe you put it down in another room," Ricky said.

They went back into the room next to the kitchen. The key wasn't anywhere.

Then they heard noises again.

"Tom, maybe someone else is in the house," Ricky said.

"Old houses make noises, Ricky," Tom said.

"Not those kinds of noises," Ricky said.

Suddenly Patches started barking.

CHAPTER 7

The Secret Door

"Patches, be quiet. Stop barking," Ricky called out.

Tom and Ricky didn't know why Patches was barking. He seemed to be barking at someone. But no one was there except Tom and Ricky.

The room they were in had lots of books. There was a big, old fireplace. Patches was barking at the fireplace.

"What's he barking at?" Tom asked.

"I wish I knew," Ricky said.

Patches got near the fireplace. He stopped barking.

"Maybe he saw a mouse," Tom said.

"I'm glad he stopped barking," Ricky said.

The house was quiet again. But Patches stayed by the fireplace. He kept trying to touch something. Suddenly Patches jumped back.

All of a sudden Tom and Ricky heard noises. They were not like the other noises they had heard. They were coming from the wall by the fireplace. All the books on the wall were moving. There were more noises.

"Look! The wall is moving. It's like a door," Ricky said.

"Patches must have touched something that made the wall open that way," Tom said.

The wall slowly moved open.

Ricky could see past the wall. "Look. There are stairs behind that wall!"

"That must be the staircase that Mr. Bell could never find," Tom said.

Patches ran through the door and up the stairs.

"Patches! Come back!" Ricky yelled.

Patches didn't come back.

"Come on, Ricky. We'd better get him," Tom said.

They walked slowly to the door. It was dark but they could see the stairs.

Then they saw some light at the top of the stairs. There must be a room or a window up there. Patches was still barking.

"Patches. Patches. Come on down," Ricky called. But Patches didn't come.

They slowly walked up the stairs.

When they got to the top, they were in a little room with a small window. They saw Patches. There were a lot of boxes in the room. Then they saw a man.

"You must be the two boys that my grandfather likes," the man said.

"Are you Mr. Bell's grandson?" Ricky asked.

"Yes. I'm Steve Bell. I'm just getting a few things. Then I'll be leaving," he said.

"Why don't you wait for Mr. Bell to come back home?" Tom asked.

"Shut up!" Steve said.

"Wait a minute. This must be the staircase Mr. Bell could never find," Tom said.

"The room with the gold," Ricky said.

"Look. I told you two to shut up. Get out of this house," he yelled.

Ricky gave Steve a hard push.

"Come on! Quick! Let's get out of here," Ricky called. Then he, Tom, and Patches all ran down the stairs.

Steve started after them. He slipped and fell all the way down. He didn't move. "Help me. Help me. I'm hurt," he yelled.

*"This must be the secret staircase
Mr. Bell could never find!"*

CHAPTER 8

Another Surprise

"Don't worry, boys," a voice said.

Tom and Ricky turned around. There was a policeman with a gun.

"Steve Bell is wanted by the police. We have been after him for a long time," the policeman said.

"Where did you come from?" Tom asked.

"We've been watching this house. We knew Steve was in town. We knew he would come here to see Mr. Bell," the policeman said.

"Help me. I'm hurt," Steve said.

"You boys come with me," the policeman said.

Tom, Ricky, and Patches went with the policeman. He went and called for more police.

"It looks like you two really helped Mr. Bell," the policeman said.

"Well, Patches helped, too," Ricky said.

"How did you find a way to open the secret door?" the policeman asked.

"Patches touched something by the fireplace. That made the wall open," Ricky said.

"I bet Mr. Bell had looked for years to find that door," the policeman said.

Other police came and took Steve away.

"I'm going to the hospital to see Mr. Bell. You boys can see him when he gets home in a few days," the policeman said.

Two days later Mr. Bell got out of the hospital. Tom and Ricky went to see him.

"We still have some more work to do in the yard, Mr. Bell," Ricky said.

"Well, now I can pay you," he said. He gave them each $50.

"Now you can fix your wheel," Tom said.

"You boys helped me a lot. I am going to have the house fixed up. It needs a lot of work. It will look just the way it looked years ago," he said.

"Where is all the gold?" Ricky asked.

He gave them each fifty dollars
and a big bag of bones for Patches.

"The bank has it now. It will be safe there. You know, I didn't think there was any gold in the house. Steve thought there was gold," Mr. Bell said.

Tom and Ricky started to leave.

"Wait a minute. The police said that Patches helped find the hidden staircase. Is that right?" Mr. Bell called out.

"Yes, it is," Ricky said.

"Well, here is a big bag of bones for him," Mr. Bell said.

Tom and Ricky laughed. Patches barked. They went home with the money and the bones. They had all made a new friend.